LIFT EVERY VOICE
AND SING

LIFT EVERY VOICE AND SING:

Words and Music

by James Weldon Johnson *and* J. Rosamond Johnson

Illustrated by Mozelle Thompson

Historical Introduction by
Mrs. Augusta Baker

Simple Piano Arrangement with Guitar Chords by
Charity Bailey

Hawthorn Books, Inc.   Publishers · New York

Facsimile of the first edition of the song

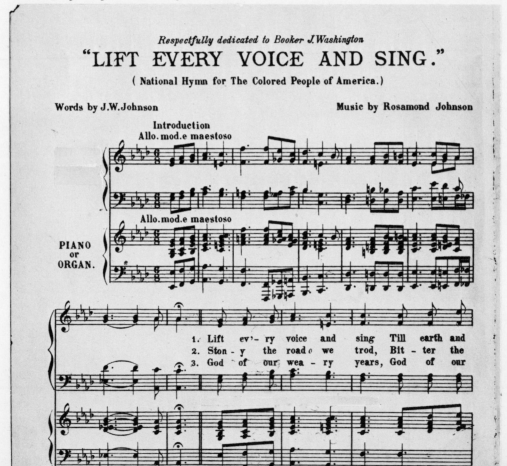

ABOUT THE SONG
AND THE BROTHERS WHO WROTE IT

James Weldon Johnson 1871–1938
J. Rosamond Johnson 1873–1954

James Weldon Johnson and his brother, John Rosamond, were born in Jacksonville, Florida. Their father was head-waiter at the best resort hotel and absolute monarch of the dining room. Their mother had been born in the Bahamas and educated in New York City. She had been the first black woman to teach in a public school in Florida.

The family often made music together. Mrs. Johnson was a trained singer and taught the boys their notes almost as soon as she taught them to read. The two brothers loved to stand at either end of the family piano and harmonize with their mother as she played and sang the old hymns, spirituals and art songs. Mr. Johnson would join them with his guitar. Although Mr. Johnson had no formal schooling, he was an extremely well-read man, and James remembered galloping about the house as an eight year old parroting his father and shouting, "My kingdom for a horse," from Shakespeare's *Richard III,* long before he knew its source. Their mother read aloud to them often, and when they were small, the boys would lie awake wondering what adventures Dickens planned next for Copperfield, or how a favorite Grimm's fairy tale would end.

When James finished Stanton grammar school in Jacksonville, there was no high school for black children in the entire state of Florida so his father decided to send him to the college-preparatory course at Atlanta University. Within a year he was enrolled as a regular college student. It was there that he became seriously interested in writing.

When he completed his studies, James became principal of Stanton school and soon made it into a high school. His brother Rosamond spent six years in Boston studying music and working. Then he returned home and became a music teacher. The brothers began working together, and J. Rosamond set several of James Weldon's poems to music. Both of them began to realize the importance of black culture and folk art, and this realization influenced their work. Over the years, James became a prominent figure in the struggle for equal rights and was one of the founders of the National Association for the Advancement of Colored People, (NAACP).

Of all the songs the brothers wrote together "Lift Every Voice and Sing" became the one which made the most lasting contribution to the musical world and to black culture.

In his autobiography *Along This Way,* James wrote of the song's creation: "A group of young men decided to hold on February 12 (1900) a celebration of Lincoln's birthday. I was put down for an address, which I began preparing; but I wanted to do something else also. My thoughts began buzzing around a central idea of writing a poem on Lincoln, but I couln't net them . . . . My central idea, however, took on another form. I talked over with my brother the idea I had in mind, and we planned to write a song to be sung as part of the exercises. We planned, better still, to have it sung by school children—a chorus of five hundred voices. . . .

"The song was taught to the children and sung very effectively at the celebration; and my brother and I went on with other work. . . . But the school children of Jacksonville kept singing the song; some of them went off to other schools and kept singing it; some of them became school teachers and taught it to their pupils. Within twenty years, the song was being sung in schools and churches and on special occasions throughout the South and in some other parts of the country . . . and is now quite generally used throughout the country as the 'Negro National Anthem.'

"Recently I spoke for the summer labor school at Bryn Mawr College and was surprised to hear it fervently sung by the white students there and to see it in their mimeographed folio of songs.

"Nothing that I have done has paid me back so fully in satisfaction as being part creator of this song. I am always thrilled deeply when I hear it sung by Negro children. I am lifted up on their voices. . . . My brother and I, in talking, have often marveled at the results that have followed what we consider an incidental effort. . . . The only comment we can make is that we wrote better than we knew."

Indeed they did. The depth and power of "Lift Every Voice" has spanned the generations. Popular entertainers record it; choral groups include it in their concerts; it has been reprinted in many song books; a black radio station signs off with it every night. But most important, *people* sing it. Wherever people, young and old, black and white, gather together in fellowship, sooner or later they are sure to lift their voices and sing this song of faith and courage, hope and joy.

AUGUSTA BAKER
Coordinator of Children's Services
The New York Public Library

Lift ev'ry voice and sing
   Till earth and heaven ring,
   Ring with the harmonies of Liberty;

Let our rejoicing rise
  High as the list'ning skies,
  Let it resound loud as the rolling sea.

Sing a song full of the faith that the dark past has taught us

Sing a song full of the hope that the present has brought us;

Facing the rising sun
   Of our new day begun,
   Let us march on till victory is won.

Stony the road we trod,
　Bitter the chast'ning rod
　Felt in the days when hope unborn had died;

Yet, with a steady beat,
Have not our weary feet
Come to the place for which our fathers sighed?

We have come over a way that with tears has been watered

We have come, treading our path thro' the blood of the slaughtered,

Out from the gloomy past,
Till now we stand at last
Where the white gleam of our bright star is cast.

God of our weary years,
God of our silent tears,
Thou who hast brought us thus far on the way;

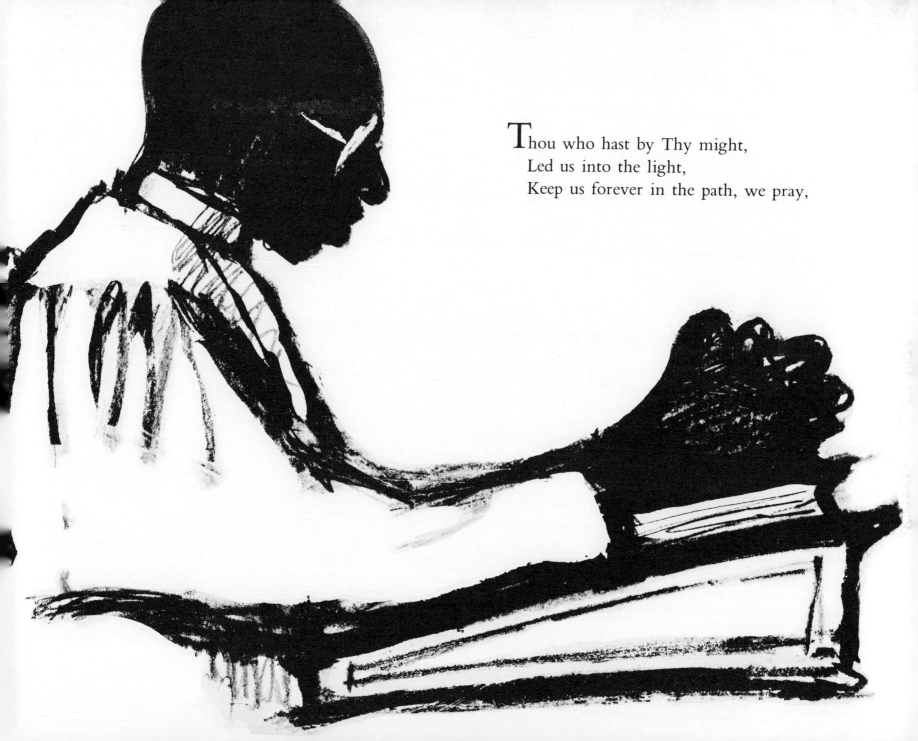

Thou who hast by Thy might,
Led us into the light,
Keep us forever in the path, we pray,

Lest our feet stray from the places, our God, where we met Thee,

Lest our hearts, drunk with the wine of the world, we forget Thee;

Shadowed beneath Thy hand,
May we forever stand,
True to our God, true to our Native land.

LIFT EVERY VOICE AND SING

Simple Piano Arrangement with Guitar Chords by Charity Bailey
Music: J. Rosamond Johnson   *Lyrics:* James Weldon Johnson

us; Fac-ing the ris - ing sun of our new day be - gun, Let us march on till vic-to - ry ___ is won.

Stony the road we trod,
   Bitter the chast'ning rod,
Felt in the days when hope unborn had died;

Yet with a steady beat,
   Have not our weary feet
Come to the place for which our fathers sighed?

We have come over a way that with tears has been watered;
We have come, treading our path thro' the blood of the slaughtered,

Out from the gloomy past.
   Till now we stand at last
Where the white gleam of our bright star is cast.

God of our weary years,
   God of our silent tears,
Thou who hast brought us thus far on the way;

Thou who hast by Thy might,
   Led us into the light,
Keep us forever in the path, we pray.

Lest our feet stray from the places, our God, where we met Thee,
Lest our hearts, drunk with the wine of the world, we forget Thee;

Shadowed beneath Thy hand,
   May we forever stand
True to our God, True to our native land.

About the Artist

Mozelle Thompson was born in Pittsburgh, Pennsylvania, and graduated from the Parsons School of Design in New York. After study in Europe he began a career as an illustrator, working on record covers, posters for Broadway shows, and a children's book, *Pumpkinseeds,* published in 1969.

While he was working on the illustrations for *Lift Every Voice and Sing,* Mr. Thompson died suddenly. His illustrations have been reproduced as he left them, with only slight finishing touches, done by his sister, Mrs. Algatha Campbell.

Tuesday Magazine